OSCAR'S
Very Grateful Day!

written by Nandhini Manikhavel
illustrated by Marty Petersen

MW00934805

Oscar's Very Grateful Day! © Copyright 2023 Nandhini Manikhavel

All rights reserved. No part of this publication may be reproduced, distributed or transmitted in any form or by any means, including photocopying, recording, or other electronic or mechanical methods, without the prior written permission of the publisher, except in the case of brief quotations embodied in critical reviews and certain other noncommercial uses permitted by copyright law.

ISBN: 979-8-88759-549-8 (paperback)
ISBN: 979-8-88759-615-0 (hardcover)
ISBN: 979-8-88759-550-4 (ebook)

This book belongs to-

Dedication & Acknowledgements

To Sruthi and Om
Be grateful for everything you've received, and
in turn enjoy the "love of GIVING"!

To my dear husband
Thanks for supporting me in this whole book journey!
Also a heart-felt thanks to my parents, family and friends,
who believed in me.

To my illustrator and new friend, Marty
Thanks for bringing life into my story and continuously
inspiring me with your artwork and beyond!

About the author

Nandhini Manikhavel was born in India, studied for her master's in the UK and moved into USA in 2008. Between corporate jobs, she worked part time volunteering in kid's school and community jobs that made her realize how much passion she felt for writing her own children's book. Her parents encouraged her to tell endless stories from a young age.

Nandhini encourages children to experience gratefulness towards every thing, starting with family and continuing to the world they belong to.

She is blessed with a beautiful family- her husband (Maheshkumar), daughter (Sruthi), son (Om), and their pet dog (Cosmo).

Nandhini loves to spend time outdoors, enjoying nature, she loves gardening, arts and crafts work. Most of all, she loves to make even a small difference in a child's life with her book. She hopes this book will inspire you to be GRATEFUL!!!

To learn more about the author and upcoming books, please visit-
www.highmindsconnect.com

About the Illustrator

Marty Petersen grew up drawing, painting, sculping & carving anything he could get his hands on; luckily his parents supported this and allowed him to continue to develop along the artistic vein.

Marty attended Kendall School of Design in Michigan, receiving degrees in both Illustration and Commercial Art. He then moved to Colorado with a fellow Kendall graduate & formed an Ad Agency in Aspen. Marty worked as designer/illustrator for several years, also carving signs for local businesses & restaurants, before relocating to the Colorado Front Range where he resides now. Best known as the artist that illustrated the "Justification For Higher Education" poster, his first love is illustrating children's stories.

To learn more about the illustrator and view his work, please visit-
www.martyart.com

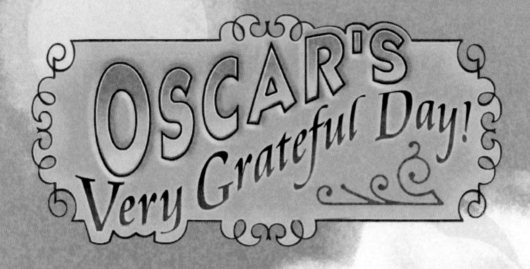

Oscar lived with his beautiful family— his mom, dad, big sister, and their pet dog.

Oscar loved watching TV programs about traveling and reading books about various places.

Oscar's family would often go on vacations to various places from beaches to mountains, from palaces to historical places, and hiking and cabin vacations to adventure trips.

Summer break was about to start. It was Oscar's final week of school before break.

Oscar began thinking about places that he would love to go that summer. He started putting together a wish list for his summer travels.

That night at the family dinner table, he talked about their summer family vacation. Everyone shared what they wanted to do, and they all discussed their options.

Oscar learned about fish that live around coral reefs at school, so he wanted to go see coral reefs. The whole family loved the idea of snorkeling at a coral reef.

The following week, mom was told that that summer was going to be particularly busy at work. She told her family that she couldn't go on a big vacation, and would only have time for a closer short weekend trip.

Dad didn't want to do a big vacation with Mom stuck at work, so they decided to postpone the coral reef trip to the following summer and take a camping trip this summer instead.

Oscar was so upset that he went to bed
early that evening, still thinking about
a coral reef vacation.

He was still upset the next day and didn't utter a word during the breakfast. Mom tried to explain her situation about why she couldn't do a big vacation, but Oscar didn't care.

A few days into summer break, Oscar's family packed their camping gear into the car for the weekend trip. Oscar refused to come, wanting to stay at home instead. After a long talk, he got into the car with much hesitation.

His sister understood her parents' situation and just enjoyed the moment. She had so much fun on the camping trip.

Oscar remained upset until one day while he was playing with his school friend David, in their neighborhood park.

Oscar said that "he really wanted to go on a vacation to see a coral reef, but instead they went on a camping trip."

David immediately said, "You are so lucky to go camping with your family. I wish I could get to go on even a day trip with my family.

It's not the same ever since my parents got divorced. My mom is working two jobs and she doesn't have time to take us out anymore. I always think of the days that my parents used to take us to movies, picnics, and the zoo. My sister is too little to even remember those days."

Oscar started to feel bad about how he behaved with his family over the coral reef vacation he had wanted.

That night, Oscar was quiet at dinner. Mom and Dad came into Oscar's room to give him a kiss good night.

Oscar said softly, "I'm sorry Mom and Dad".

Mom asked, "Why?" Oscar told them about David and about how he couldn't go on even a day trip with his own family.

Mom tucked Oscar in and said, "There are a lot of families who can't go on trips because they don't have any extra money, time or for other reasons."

Oscar felt so grateful for everything he got,
and understood that he won't always
get what he wants.

Oscar said, "Thanks for taking us on the
camping trip," to his Mom and Dad.
Dad told him, "I'm so proud of my big boy"
with a hug and a smile.

A few weeks later, Mom's job became less busy, and the family was able to take their trip to the coral reef that summer after all!

Oscar came back home from his coral reef trip, and invited David over for a play date that weekend.

Oscar took a lot of videos of his trip to create
a beautiful movie for David!

Watching the movie, David felt just like he was right there with Oscar on the trip!

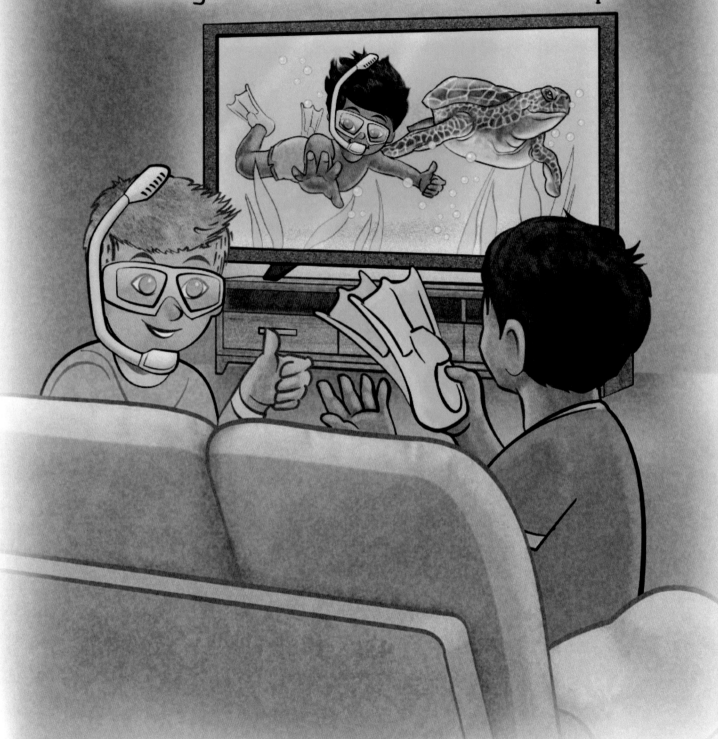

David thanked Oscar for sharing his grand adventure.

After David left from their playdate,
Oscar's parents said, "You are a
very good friend!"

From then on, Oscar started making videos of each and every one of his adventures, to share with his friends and family!

Download the
Gratitude Activities and Games for Free!

To say thanks for purchasing this book, I would like
to give you a few activity pages and games
for free!

This resource will help your child think, how THANKFUL
& GRATEFUL they are for everything in their life!

Visit http://www.highmindsconnect.com/

Made in the USA
Las Vegas, NV
15 April 2023

70620774R00019